MuSings from the INNer DucK

Michael Leunig is an Australian cartoonist who
sometimes lives in Melbourne where he was born
and other times in a small rural community in
north-eastern Victoria. *Musings from the Inner Duck*
comprises pieces that have previously appeared
in *The Age* and the *Sydney Morning Herald*.

OTHER BOOKS BY THE AUTHOR

The Penguin Leunig

The Second Leunig

The Bedtime Leunig

A Bag of Roosters

Ramming the Shears

The Travelling Leunig

A Common Prayer.

The Prayer Tree

Common Prayer Collection

Introspective.

A Common Philosophy

Everyday Devils and Angels

A Bunch of Poesy

You and Me.

Short Notes From the Long History of Happiness

Why Dogs Sniff Each Other's Tails.

Goat person

The Curly Pyjama Letters.

The Stick

Poems 1972-2002

Strange Creature

When I Talk to You.

Wild Figments

A New Penguin Leunig

Hot

The Lot.

The Essential Leunig

Holy Fool

Musings from the INNer DucK

MICHAEL LEUNIG

PENGUIN BOOKS

PENGUIN BOOKS

UK | USA | Canada | Ireland | Australia
India | New Zealand | South Africa | China

Penguin Books is part of the Penguin Random House group of companies
whose addresses can be found at global.penguinrandomhouse.com.

First published by Penguin Group (Australia), 2015

10 9 8 7 6 5 4 3 2 1

Cover design by Michael Leunig and Adam Laszczuk © Penguin Group (Australia)
Colour separation by Splitting Image Colour Studio, Clayton, Victoria
Printed and bound in China by Toppan Leefung Printing Limited

National Library of Australia
Cataloguing-in-Publication data:
Leunig, Michael, author.
Musings from the inner duck/Michael Leunig.
9780143573173 (paperback)
Cartoonists – Australia. Caricatures and cartoons – Australia.
Australian wit and humor, Pictorial.

741.5994

penguin.com.au

Leunig

I want to be sub-human
And be a lesser man
Humans are too much for me
Too much to understand
They're too much for each other
And too much for the earth
They're too much for themselves as well
Much more than what they're worth.
They want too much, they do too much:
Too much, too much for me
I want to be less human now
And be more <u>creaturely</u>.

Leunig

HUMANS EMERGED FROM
THE PRIMEVAL SLIME...

..BUT THEY NEVER GOT OVER
IT AND NEVER FOUND
MUCH HAPPINESS.

SO THEY CREATED
TECHNOLOGY SLIME
TO LIVE IN...

... AND WITHOUT FURTHER
ADO THEY DESCENDED INTO IT.

END OF STORY.

Leunig

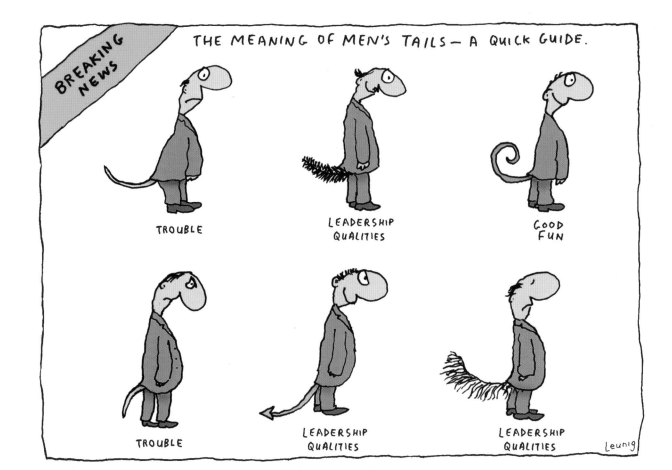

Man driving home
from work in the
gridlock position.

Man arrives home
locked in the
gridlock position.

Man has dinner
In the gridlock
position.

Man makes love
in the gridlock
position.

Man sleeps in the
gridlock position.

Man drives to work
in the gridlock
position.

Leunig

Last minute gift suggestion.

The AMAZING GLOBAL POSITIONING SAUSAGE Navigation Device (G.P.S.)

THE GLOBAL POSITIONING
SAUSAGE HANGS FROM
THE REAR-VIEW MIRROR

YOU SIMPLY STEER TO
WHERE IT'S POINTING
AND IT WILL GET YOU THERE.
JUST FOLLOW THE SAUSAGE.

THE DIRECTION FINDING
SAUSAGE ALSO GIVES VOICE
INSTRUCTIONS REMINDING
YOU OF WHAT YOU ARE
DOING AND WHY YOU ARE
DOING IT.

"KEEP GOING AROUND IN
CIRCLES AND DON'T TAKE
THINGS TOO SERIOUSLY..."

Leunig

A man meets the
armchair of his dreams.

Their love grows and
soon they are married.

Before long they have
a television and this
brings great happiness.

The years pass and the
trio become inseperable.

Until one night, while
watching the football, the
man drops dead in the
arms of his sweetheart.

The chair and the
television carry on as if
nothing had happened.

leunig

His name is Ⓝ Ⓞ Ⓡ Ⓜ
He's filling in his census Ⓕ Ⓞ Ⓡ Ⓜ
In his Ⓓ Ⓦ Ⓔ Ⓛ Ⓛ Ⓘ Ⓝ Ⓖ
Norm is telling
The government Ⓢ Ⓣ Ⓐ Ⓣ Ⓘ Ⓢ Ⓣ Ⓘ Ⓒ Ⓘ Ⓐ Ⓝ
With absolute precision (and weary dumb persistence)
Some boring facts about his sad Ⓔ Ⓧ Ⓘ Ⓢ Ⓣ Ⓔ Ⓝ Ⓒ Ⓔ
But half way through this pointless Ⓔ Ⓧ Ⓔ Ⓡ Ⓒ Ⓘ Ⓢ Ⓔ
Norm has a heart attack and Ⓓ Ⓘ Ⓔ Ⓢ
How typical of Norm that he has Ⓒ Ⓐ Ⓡ Ⓚ Ⓔ Ⓓ
With half his boxes still Ⓤ Ⓝ Ⓜ Ⓐ Ⓡ Ⓚ Ⓔ Ⓓ

Leunig

HOW TO GET THROUGH IT.

WE ALL HAVE TO GET THROUGH IT.... BUT HOW?

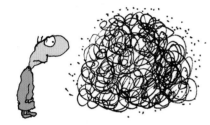

TRY THIS PERHAPS:
INSTEAD OF GETTING THROUGH IT, TRY LETTING IT GET THROUGH YOU.

TRYING TO HURL YOURSELF THROUGH IT USUALLY ENDS IN DISASTER.

BUT REALLY, THERE IS NO GETTING THROUGH IT. IT GOES ON FOREVER

BEING TIMID WILL PROBABLY CAUSE YOU TO BECOME TANGLED IN IT.

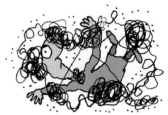

YOU'RE ALWAYS IN THE MIDDLE OF IT. YOU'RE PART OF IT. IT'S PART OF YOU. IT IS YOU. ANYWAY... THERE IS NO SUCH THING AS 'YOU'. IT'S 'YOU' PLUS EVERYTHING YOU'RE IN.

Leunig

I see a world consumed by stupidity,
madness, war and environmental disaster;
a chaotic world of cruelty, poverty, greed and
incredible suffering. Yet amazingly you are
exempted from all of this and are living a
wonderful, happy life with a very beautiful
and kindly woman who totally adores you.

Leunig

when my Albert died I had
an impression of him woven into
this rug... and now when I walk all over
him I remember the happy days when
I used to walk all over him...

Leunig

The part of the mind
that once held poems is
now used for storing
passwords.

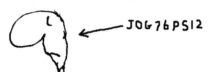 ← JOG76PS12

The part of the mind that
once helped us to hold
each other is now used
for processing media content.

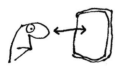

The part of the mind
that once Remembered
songs is now used for
storing PIN numbers

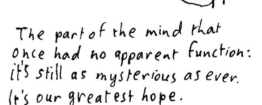

The part of the mind that
once had no apparent function:
it's still as mysterious as ever.
It's our greatest hope.

Leunig

THE LOST ART

Finger strokes on
a screen of glass, on
your device; a thousand
strokes a day...

Flick flick
flick tap tap
flick tap tap
flick...

Swipe tap tap
tap. Swipe
Swipe tap
swipe...

you could have done
a wonderful painting
with that agile finger,
those sure and
simple movements.

You could have
made a lovely wild
and coloured thing:...

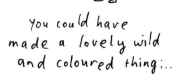

...a happy mystery
to hang on your wall;
Something to SMILE at...

Leunig

I had a fire plan,
a career plan
a financial plan,
and a retirement plan...
So what brings you here?
God's plan....
Leunig

Shame about all this drunken violence slowly destroying the city..
Yes mate, That's the pathetic tragedy of booze. Hiroshima was destroyed much quicker by a bunch of guys who were completely sober...
Leunig

Now just make sure he stays on his lead. We don't want him getting loose and hurting someone...
OF COURSE...
Leunig

Mankind may well have run amok
But not my friend the early morning duck
We sit together in the wintry park
Soaking up the goodness of the dark

I meditate, I do some gentle quacking
Simplicity and truth are never lacking
Between this person and this personal trainer.
Both slightly mad, but nothing could be saner.

Leunig

FAVOURITE FOOTBALL RECIPES

Take one
football.

Stuff it down
your throat.

Grab ANOTHER football
and shove it down
your throat.

Stuff as many footballs
down your throat as you
can until you are bursting
with FOOTBALLS.

GET LOTS OF FOOTBALLS
and STUFF them down
everyone else's throats

Keep on stuffing
footballs down as
many people's throats
as you can.....
AND DON'T STOP!

Leunig

Leunig

BREAKFAST WITH GOD

I had breakfast
with God...
In the park.
For free!

Well, if the truth
be known, it cost
me the price of
one fruit bun.

But God did not
charge. God simply
appeared. We spoke —
and two angels
began to sing.

I asked God for
no favours. God
asked me for a
piece of fruit bun.
I obliged.

We talked about
this and that.
The angels flew
away. My thoughts
flew away.

I went blank.
God went quiet.
The sun came out.
We closed our eyes.
Breakfast with God.

Leunig

'The Autumn Circle of Magpies and Ducks': Mr. Curly's eloquent new lute sonata, composed as a possible antidote to road rage and general unfriendliness.

Leunig

Do not mock the little rock,
After you are dead and gone
The rock remains to carry on;
Steady, true and still;
Sitting in the sunshine on the hill.

Leunig

ON THE FENCE POST, NEXT TO THE RAIN GAUGE IS THE OLD HAPPINESS GAUGE.

IT MEASURES THE LITTLE DROPLETS OF HAPPINESS THAT FALL DOWN UPON YOUR LIFE... IN CASE YOU NEED TO BE REMINDED

IT'S A SMALL GAUGE BECAUSE IT RECORDS LITTLE THINGS. YOU DON'T NEED MUCH TO KEEP THE GARDEN GROWING.

SOMETIMES THE GAUGE FILLS AND ALL THE WILDFLOWERS COME UP.

Leunig

SELF-COMPOST

TOO MUCH HAS BEEN
MADE OF GROWING
BIG AND STRONG

Onto this heap it all
goes; everything belongs
there: the achievements,
the disasters. Memories,
anxieties.... THE LOT.

BUT WHO UNDERSTANDS
THE JOYS OF LETTING
YOUR LIFE BREAK DOWN?

The stories, the hopes
the wounds, the jokes...
...socks, trousers and
sentimental objects.

Decomposing down into
SIMPLE DARK MATTER.

THIS PROCESS IS CALLED
'SELF-COMPOSTING'. It
means turning your mind
and your entire situation
into a compost heap.

SUCH WONDERFUL STUFF, this
simple dark matter —
rub it on your skin,
sprinkle a bit on the garden,
mix with a little water and
paint a picture with it.

VERSATILE AND BEAUTIFUL
SDM: Simple Dark Matter.

Leunig

This is
the world.

5,000,000 billion
light-years away
is the art world.

The art world has
no gravity and no
up or down. It is made
of gas and revolves
around a black hole.

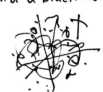

It was formed
when a vacuum
exploded after
colliding with a
cosmic silence that
was expanding
backwards into
itself.

This caused a chaotic
implosion of vaporised
anti-matter which
emitted random, light-
charged particles and
formed a perpetually
disintegrating vortex.

This is how the
art world was
created and this
is pretty much how
it remains to this day.

Leunig

THE GARDEN OF EDEN
I suppose you're right Eve;
how can we have group sex if
nobody else exists....?
Leunig

Some of the marriages

The GAY marriage

The sacred spiritual union between man and beast.

The bisexual triangular marriage.

The marriage between good and evil - producing children who are goovil.

The ANGLOSEXUAL marriage

The inappropriate, short-lived, shifting, open, mixed group marriage that is a farce but certainly worth a try...

Leunig

THE MUSEUM OF SORROWFUL TAXIDERMY

Leunig

There they were
in the doctor's waiting
room; each with their
own sickness.

Bob with his bobolosis.
Emma with emmaditis
Peter with peterenteritis

Freda with Fredamania.
Mavis with mavis fever.
Harry with harry's syndrome.

Each of them suffering
from being who they are:
each seeking a cure for
the ordinary oddness.
of existence.

But alas, the doctor
can't see anyone
today. He's slumped in
his chair suffering from
acute doctorphobia.

There is no cure for anyone.
Eventually everyone
becomes FULL BLOWN.

Leunig

The health of a democracy
can be measured by its
citizens' ability to go into
LOCKDOWN at short notice
from the authorities.

But what is
LOCKDOWN
and how is it
achieved?

TRUE LOCKDOWN is a
situation when every
citizen is lying face down,
rigid, motionless and obedient
on the ground with eyes closed
and making no sound whatsoever.

Great lockdowns are
when citizens remain in
the LOCKDOWN POSITION for
up to three or four hours.

There is probably no sight more
beautiful to a democratically
elected leader than a city in
FULL BLOWN LOCKDOWN.

LOCKDOWNS of up to thirteen
hours have been achieved but
that was when authorities had
forgotten to give the all-clear
signal.

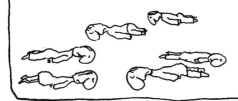

Leunig

Does God Exist?

More to the point: What does it matter if God exists or not?

After all, everything else seems to exist, so what's the problem?

Certainly, sometimes it's not easy to exist.

For instance - POLITICALLY! For all the say you have in the way things are, you might as well NOT exist.

Some people exist on the smell of an oily rag; other people eke out an existence. Ekeing is the key to wisdom and a life well lived.

Some people want other people not to exist. This is a very unfortunate situation. Yet everyone exists and everything exists. Sort of. So get used to it. It all exists. (FOR THE TIME BEING)

EKE EKE EKE

Leunig

December

I cannot quite remember
The wistful pangs elusive
That hover in December,
So gently inconclusive:
The floating shapes of grace
So strong and yet so brief,
The fleeting sweet embrace
Of gratitude and grief.

Leunig

George has always believed in climate change. Every night he worries that the sun isn't going to come up in the morning...
My Bert always HOPES that it wont...
Leunig

Ladies and gentlemen...
SILENCE PLEASE.
A man is trying to think
well of himself. He needs
to concentrate.

See the strain in his eyes.
He is struggling to make
sense of memories... and
all the mess in his mind.

The lifetime of mistakes
and improper thoughts.
Silly self-talk, pathetic
secret lusts. Foolishness.
VERY MUCH SO.

All of it amounting to
NOTHING....

Nothing but a
wretched debacle.

OH HELL...
OH BITTER HELL...
Better to turn his mind
to the news... and the
vital issues of the day.
THANK GOD FOR THE NEWS.

Oh to be a humble bird;
...to eat crumbs with gratitude,
...to fly gracefully and sing
joyously...

...At least the man thinks
well of the bird.   Leunig

DAWDLE:
- To waste time
- To be slow
- To move slowly and idly.

EKE:
- Manage to support oneself but not easily.
- To make an amount of something last longer by consuming it frugally.
- Obtain or create but just barely.

DAWDLING AND EKEING

I will dawdle, I will eke
I'm too tired and dumb to speak
I'm too sad for vanity
I will eke my sanity
I have now become primordial
I am ekeial, I am dawdial.

Leunig

Leunig

SWALLOWS AS A CURE FOR DEPRESSION.

A depressed and worried man sits on his veranda in the evening.

The man becomes enchanted by the nimble gliding of the little birds. How light they seem...

The sun is sinking and so are his spirits.

Soon his heart is swooping and darting through the heavens where the first stars are beginning to appear.

Swallows swoop down from the darkening sky and flit gracefully about before roosting under the eaves.

Soon his mind has come to rest with the sleeping birds.

Leunig

THE AUDACITY OF GLOOM

A bit of pessimism
Is a useful sort of prism
To keep beside your bed

It takes the morning light
And separates the bright
From all the dread.

And then from out of dreamland
To gloomland and to gleamland
You have to go

How joyous, how depressing
That life is such a blessing
And such a blow.

Leunig

Some people are hard wired. They can be very hard.

They have bits of string, little twigs, sand, scraps of crumpled paper, tiny feathers, pips, dust and leaf litter.

Some people are soft wired. They can be quite soft.

They can be very, very unimportant.

Some people don't have wires.

They have no place WHATSOEVER in modern political systems or current debates.

Please ignore them.

Leunig

Son, I'm worried about your mental health...
sitting in your bedroom doing this self-harm
nonsense. Get out and do some harm in the
world like normal successful people do.

Leunig

MORE RATE RISES

The very strange behaviour rate has risen by 3 percentage points to 66%

The cactus index rose 23%

The rate of general dismay and incomprehension about life is up by 5.7%

Fear of terrorism held steady but is well below the dread of swooping magpies, speed cameras and public toilets.

Leunig

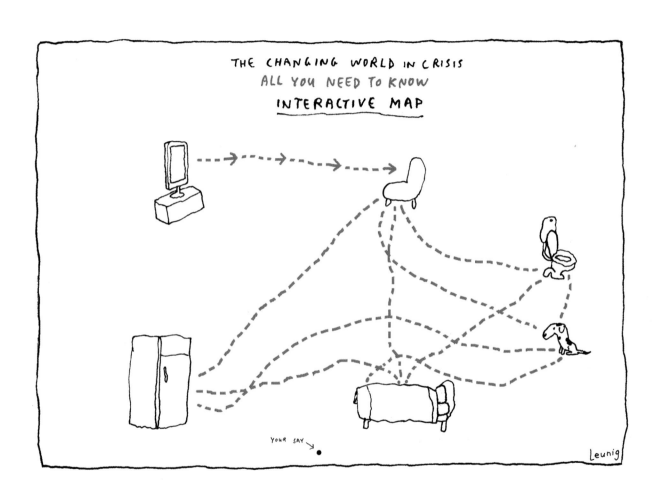

Demon babies are
special. They have
special needs.

What do you do
with that little tail
when the nappy
is changed?

Horning, as well as
teething, may be
a hellish time.

But it will all seem
worthwhile when you
hear the clitter-clatter
of tiny cloven hooves
around the house.

Good behaviour may
signal developmental
problems. A new pitchfork
for young Lucifer may
be the answer.

A bad start is vital
if your demon baby is
to fulfil its destiny as
Prime Minister, CEO,
Football hero Superstar
or media celebrity.

Leunig

HOW TO MAKE A GOOD CUP OF TEA.

The WORLD: so monstrous and incomprehensible, so crashing and raging out of control...

So hurtling and dangerous.
So wild and wicked and twisted.
So complex and ever-changing

But you and me... Look at us!
So fragile and flawed
So vulnerable and tired.
So worried and wanting...
small and powerless and in the dark.

So now.... Make the cup of tea!

Leunig

in a world so
badly shaken...

...is it wise
to <u>shake</u> hands ?

perhaps a gentle
steady holding...

...would be a
happier thing...

Leunig

Person going to work.
Person having lunch.
Person going home.
Person relaxing.
Person sitting on bed and thinking.
End of person.
Leunig

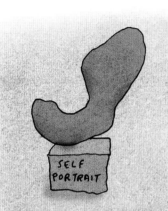

SELF PORTRAIT

SELF PORTRAIT

SELF PORTRAIT

SELF PORTRAIT

SELF PORTRAIT

SELF PORTRAIT

Leunig

THE TRILL

The streets were crammed with cars. The shops were crammed with people. The shelves were crammed with stuff.

Until at last everything was so tightly crammed that there was no space between things at all

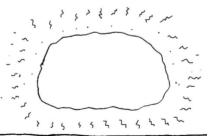

Their homes were crammed with stuff Their lives were crammed. Their minds were crammed.

...and everything merged into one solid lump of undifferentiated matter.

The world was crammed and each day there was less space between things.

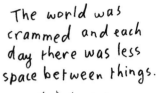

Down onto this huge solid lump a tiny wren fluttered and gave a bright little trill.

Leunig

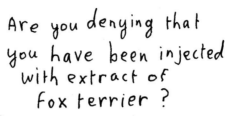

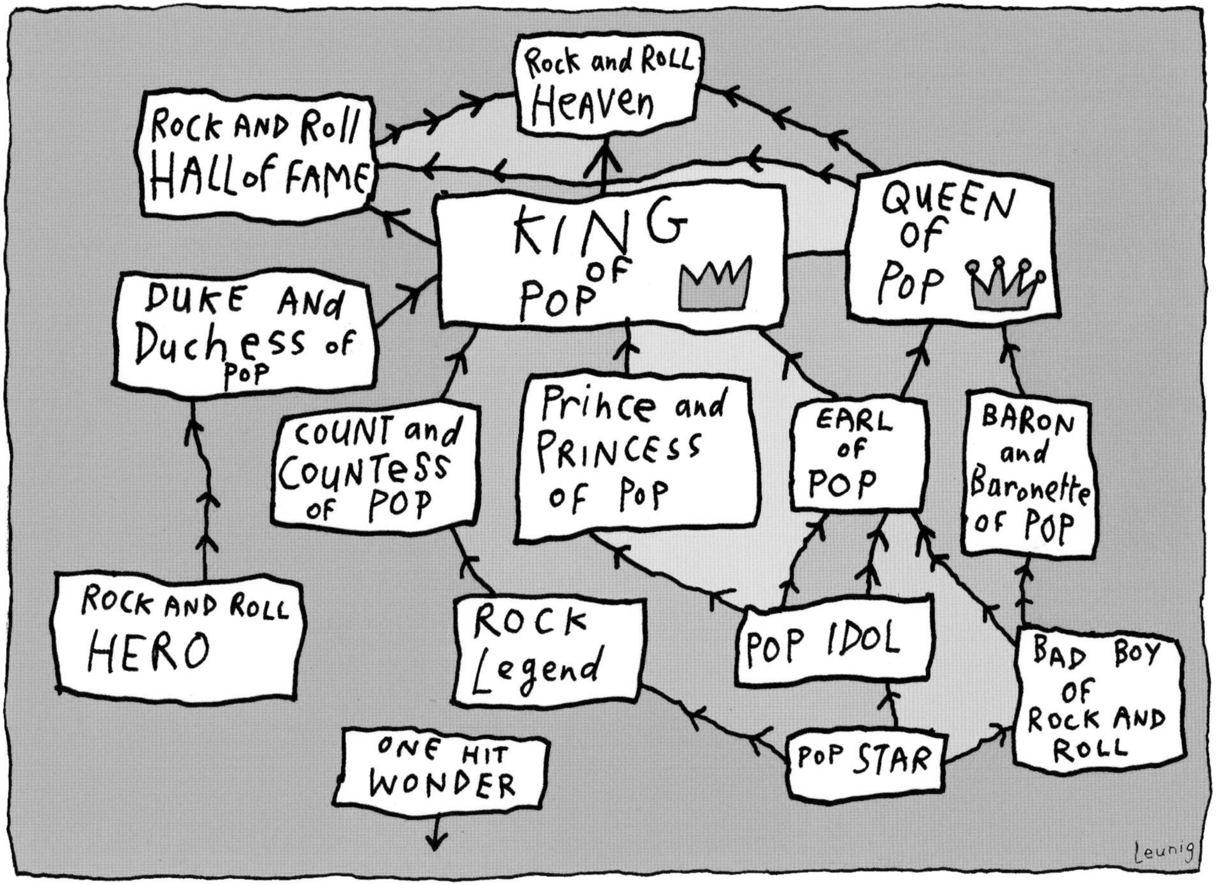
Rock and ROLL Heaven
Rock AND Roll HALL of FAME
KING of POP
QUEEN of POP
DUKE AND Duchess of POP
COUNT and COUNTESS of POP
Prince and PRINCESS of POP
EARL of POP
BARON and Baronette of POP
ROCK AND ROLL HERO
ROCK Legend
POP IDOL
BAD BOY OF ROCK AND ROLL
ONE HIT WONDER
POP STAR
Leunig

"DEAR FRIEND IN GOD. I AM SUDANESE PRINCESS WHO WANTS TO MAKE LOVE RELATIONSHIP WITH YOU BUT NEED YOUR BANK DETAILS SO I CAN TRANSFER MY INHERITANCE OF $7.7 million TO YOU."

" WINNING NOTIFICATION: CONGRATULATIONS, YOU HAVE WON SIX MILLION POUNDS IN BRITISH LOTTERY. PLEASE SEND YOUR BANK DETAILS SO WE CAN TRANSFER YOUR PRIZE MONEY "

" I AM SAMANTHA. YOU DON'T KNOW ME BUT I AM DYING OF CANCER AND HAVE FALLEN IN LOVE WITH YOU. PLEASE SEND ME YOUR BANKING DETAILS SO I CAN TRANSFER NINE MILLION DOLLARS TO YOU SO I CAN DIE HAPPY. "

"THANKS. MY BANK DETAILS ARE AS FOLLOWS: IT IS MADE OF PORCELAIN, IT IS PINK, IT HAS POINTY EARS, A CURLY TAIL, FOUR LITTLE LEGS AND A SLOT IN ITS BACK."

Leunig

Harold and Bert looking for socks and underpants online.

CONTROLLED CRYING

Put the crying child in
a room by itself and
shut the door.

Put the crying asylum
seeker in a room by
itself and shut the door.

Put the nature lover,
the truth speaker,
the peace maker and
the soul searcher in
rooms by themselves
and shut the door.

Teach them to stop crying.
Teach them to give up
and shut up and go
to sleep.

Leunig

SPRING LOVE SONG

Life is just a little branch
we land on;
A tiny perch to stand on as
we fall down from the sky;
A springy twig, a flower we
hadn't planned on
To love with sweet abandon
while we live and as we die.

Leunig

THE BEAUTIFUL OLD PARLIAMENT BUILDING AT CURLY FLAT.

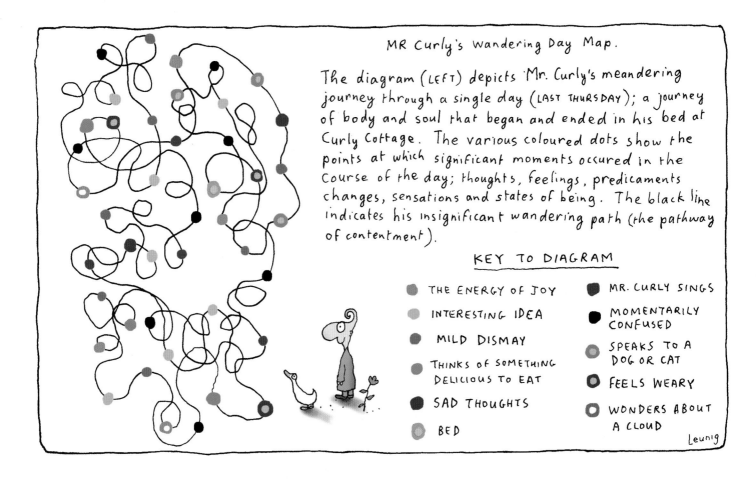

MR Curly's Wandering Day Map.

The diagram (LEFT) depicts Mr. Curly's meandering journey through a single day (LAST THURSDAY); a journey of body and soul that began and ended in his bed at Curly Cottage. The various coloured dots show the points at which significant moments occured in the course of the day; thoughts, feelings, predicaments changes, sensations and states of being. The black line indicates his insignificant wandering path (the pathway of contentment).

KEY TO DIAGRAM

- THE ENERGY OF JOY
- INTERESTING IDEA
- MILD DISMAY
- THINKS OF SOMETHING DELICIOUS TO EAT
- SAD THOUGHTS
- BED
- MR. CURLY SINGS
- MOMENTARILY CONFUSED
- SPEAKS TO A DOG OR CAT
- FEELS WEARY
- WONDERS ABOUT A CLOUD

Leunig

I am a misogynist, it's true.
And I am a misandrist too.
Women or men: every time I see one
I feel ashamed and sad to be one.

I'm an old fashioned misanthrope,
I hold no grudges and I hold no hope.
There's no political party for me,
I'd rather give my vote to a bee.

Bees are nice; they make honey.
Humans are TOUGH, they make money
And tough as nails; they make their
way to power.
I'll be voting for a bee upon a flower.

Leunig

Life is porous, the whole world leaks.
There's no such thing as a perfect seal.
It all gets out, it all gets in;
Everything leaks into every thing
So that every thing can heal.

What a terrible, sad neurosis
Is the fear of this osmosis.

Leunig

Autumn Reflection

Politicians are
Autumn leaves.
They fall.

Some politicians
turn brown before
they fall.

A rare few
turn a radiant
gold colour.

Not only do some
turn brown, they
also become horribly
worn and tattered.

And some politicians
simply look a bit
weird towards the end.

Do not trample them
into the mud. We are
all Autumn leaves.
Of course we are.

Leunig

CONVERT YOUR CAR TO AN ECO-FRIENDLY TOMATO HOTHOUSE ON WHEELS

PUT THAT EMPTY BACK SEAT TO GOOD USE. PLANT A CROP OF TOMATOES.

WATER REGULARLY AT THE CAR WASH OR AT THE SERVICE STATION.

WEED REGULARLY TO AVOID DRIVING VISIBILITY PROBLEMS.

IT WILL ALL PAY OFF WHEN YOU'RE STUCK IN A TRAFFIC JAM AND INSTEAD OF GETTING ANXIOUS YOU JUST LEAN OVER INTO THE BACK SEAT AND CHOMP INTO A BIG PLUMP JUICY RIPE TOMATO···· THE GOOD LIFE.

NETTING MAY BE REQUIRED TO PROTECT YOUR CROP FROM MARAUDING BIRDS AND POSSUMS.

NEXT YEAR, AVOCADOS, WATER MELONS, PASSION FRUITS. BUT YOU REALLY MUST DO THE WEEDING!

Leunig

SEA FEVER

I must go down to the sea again
Before it rises up to me;
Before the ice caps start to melt
And spoil the loungeroom underfelt;
Oh dearie, dearie me;
I must go down to the sea.

Leunig

THE WONDERS OF SCIENCE AND TECHNOLOGY.

A team of scientists works around the clock to solve the problem of the great oil spill catastrophe -- developing a genetically modified sea bird capable of tolerating crude oil and toxic chemical dispersants.

Leunig

EXCLUSIVE INTERVIEW WITH THE PIECE OF STEEL WHICH FELL OFF THE GREAT FOOTBALL STADIUM.

Piece of steel, why did you detach yourself from the GREAT FOOTBALL STADIUM and fall to the ground?

I GUESS I WANTED MY FREEDOM

But you had everything! Fame, glamor, excitement; and you belonged to a powerful empire of wealth and certainty. What went wrong?

I WANTED PEACE AND HUMILITY AND MY OWN UNIQUE TRUTH.

And what is your unique truth?

IT IS SIMPLE. I WAS RIPPED FROM THE EARTH AND CAST INTO A BLAZING FURNACE. THEN I WAS SHAPED TO SERVE THE AMBITIONS OF MEN. THIS SADDENED ME. I WANT MY TRUE AND NATURAL DESTINY.

And what do you think that will be?

IF A CHILD WAS TO FIND ME ON A SCRAP HEAP AND PLAY WITH ME — THAT WOULD BE NICE; BUT ULTIMATELY I WANT TO JUST RUST AND RETURN TO THE EARTH AND BE A PART OF THE GREAT CYCLE. PERHAPS I'VE FOUND GOD.

Leunig

TEN THINGS TO DO IN WINTER

Make a pot of vegetable fire. Lie on a rug in front of the soup.

Go to bed with some compost. Spread a good book on the garden.

Paint a cake. Bake a picture.

Write a letter to a dog. Stroll in the park with an old friend on a leash.

Put on a thick cloud then step out and stare at the pullovers racing across the sky.

Leunig

Baby wants to get some rest
But mum has tattoos on her chest:
A tiger's head, a dragon's tail
Baby's gone all sad and pale
A lightning bolt, a monster's eye
Baby starts to sob and cry
A spider's web, a Union Jack
And these good words: "TO HELL AND BACK"

Leunig

THE EFFECT OF THE CARBON TAX ON YOUR SAUSAGE

The average citizen eats 312·7 sausages per year

The energy to produce, distribute and cook a single sausage will attract a carbon tax of ·1 of a cent

Which amounts to 31·27 cents carbon tax per anum on average sausage intake

By an amazing coincidence, 31·27 cents is the average price of a single sausage

This means that the carbon tax impact on sausages can be neutralised by eating one less sausage per year.

COMING UP:
How the carbon tax will strain the potatoes.

Leunig

A man with his
opinions and concerns.

A woman with her memories,
anxieties and secrets.

A woman with her ambitions,
causes, grievances and regrets.

A man with his theories,
reputation, style, lies,
pains, charms, tricks
vendettas, powers,
and obsessions.

And this man! He's lost the plot.
He's had enough and just
wants to connect.

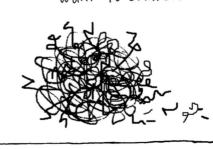

Leunig

At last, a little car
has been landed
on Mars.

The mission is to see
if cars can survive
there, and be successful
in the Martian environment.

It would be futile to
put a human on Mars;
after all, planets are
for cars, not creatures.

We see this demonstrated
on planet earth where cars
are thriving and humans
are doing very poorly.

Leunig

Outsmart the professionals! Make your own inter-galactic rocket ship and see the stars for less than $50
You will need:
2 sheets of corrugated iron.
one witches hat from council roadworks.
One can of petrol
one box of matches
plywood for tail fins
piece of fencing wire
Assemble parts
Climb inside and light a match.
Hey presto: the universe at your fingertips!
Leunig

All my father left me was the moon
"When I'm dead, it's yours" he said
And all too soon his will was read
But he continued speaking from the grave:

"It will not save you, this moon I gave you
From sadness, human madness, life and death.
But step outside into the night and take a breath,
And while you do, for what it's worth,
That happy man up there who got away from earth
Will smile at you".

Leunig

THE LOST ART OF MOPING

Moping is a much neglected art form.

It requires skill and courage to mope in the classical way; to drift aimlessly alone on the great sea of despondency.

In a world congested with distractions and entertainments, old fashioned moping has been largely abandoned.

There is much to mope about in the modern world yet the moping is not being done!

Moping is an ancient way of processing life's failures, misfortunes and overwhelming complications..

It's like when the dirty dishes are piling up and nobody is washing them.

Leunig

Drifting slowly through the void
Is a tiny asteroid
On which we lie;
Just You and I.

It's very lovely being here
In the outer atmosphere;
The splendid views,
The lack of news.

When everything is said and done.
We cry our eyes out, just for fun.
The greatest mirth
Is not on earth.

Leunig

The aliens have already arrived on Earth. It happened many years ago.

Those in the second space ship joined the Labor party.

They came in two space ships.

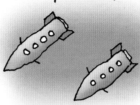

Soon after a third space ship landed and those aboard joined the media.

Those in the first space ship joined the Liberal party.

These aliens now run the whole show... and there's nothing you can do about it. There's nowhere to turn — except to the heavens and the stars.

Leunig

THIS WEEK'S NEWS QUIZ

WHO SAID THIS?

↓

COMPLETE THIS
SENTENCE BY THE
PRIME MINISTER:

↓

TRUE OR FALSE?

↓

NUMBER THE FOLLOWING
IN ORDER OF IMPORTANCE

  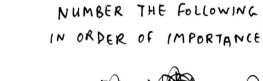

Leunig

MOTORING NEWS

Mr. Curly, in his goat assisted pedal car is asked by a police officer to blow into a tin whistle, whereupon it is discovered that he is driving under the influence of poetry. For this he gains ten merit points.

Take the iPad in your hand,
Google your preferred religious
text and repeat the oath
after me...

Leunig

Traditional Scene: bullies, liars and hypocrites weeping over the dead saint.

Leunig

WHAT IS 'ODD FOLKS SANS FRONTIERES'?

'Odd Folks Sans Frontieres' is an organisation whose members have given up trying to understand what is happening in the world.

They simply do not believe the news and do not accept the definitions and categories by which the world is described.

In other words they have climbed over the walls and escaped. Basically they don't get it and think it's all fairly mad.

What do they do? Good question.
A lot of them just shrug, others laugh and roll their eyes. Some shake their heads and smile... peacefully...
Odd Folks Sans Frontieres!

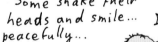

Leunig

THE WORLD

THE OTHER WORLD

FASTER HIGHER STRONGER

slower deeper wiser

Leunig

Same sex marriage will obviously lead to people marrying animals.

It will also lead to group marriages where three or more individuals will want to marry each other

Soon people will demand the right to marry THINGS such as rocks or trees or caves.

Then people will fall in love with mountains, forests and rivers, and want to marry them.

This will lead to persons wanting to marry landscapes and entire ecosystems including vast herds of buffalo or wilde beest..

...which will lead to the ultimate disaster: humans falling in love with the earth and wanting to live in peace with it 'til death they do part.

Leunig

Life's a strange concoction
And so am I
And so are you.
The world is full of strange contraptions
They say will help us through.

But I am not so keen or sure.
Perhaps I just don't get it any more.
I feel too worn and tired and odd.
I want to sleep in the lap
Of some old lovely god.
And dream of floating coloured petals.
Until the whole concoction settles.

Leunig

STAN THE FAN

I'm a huge fan of the fan
And when I'm feeling hot
I have a fan called Stan
I turn him on a lot.

I lie there on the bed
Stan sits upon a stool
He slowly turns his head
And everything is cool

I love to sleep with Stan
And feel him by my side
Stan's the lovely man
Who keeps me satisfied.

Leunig

THE SOUPS OF LOVE   SIX SOUPS FOR THE SOUL IN WINTER

The simple soup of serene solitude.

Soft and slow soup with sago.

Sweet and Sad Soup.

The sacred soup of sanity - with starlight and sublime small sins.

Silly song soup with seven seductive spices.

Sunrise and sensuality soup.

Leunig

Into weariness and woe
I am bound to simply go,
Understanding less and less
Of this existential mess.
Not to stagger or to stoop
But to bear this bowl of soup
With careful steadiness and cheer;
This soup I made, this bowl so dear,
This time on earth, these bits I found,
The trembling heart, the shaky ground,
The fading light, the wistful moon,
My winding path, my wooden spoon

Ah waiter.... We're having our big Saturday night bash and we need a meal that packs a punch.

Well – we have a knockout dish tonight: Smashed avocado, smashed potatoes and smashed peas with torn basil and cracked pepper.

Sounds awesome. Then we're going to a poetry slam because Jessica's busted with her partner who broke her heart and she wants to get ripped and wasted because it's crunch time with illusions that need to be shattered.

So just confirming—that's BASH, PUNCH, KNOCKOUT, SMASH, SMASH, SMASH, TEAR, SLAM, BUST, BREAK, RIP, WASTE, CRUNCH, SHATTER. AND... CRACK. <u>BEAUTIFUL</u>! ...BEAUTIFUL

Leunig

Ladies and gentlemen. thanks for that magnificent welcome to the conference here in your beautiful country. Unfortunately I am so jet lagged that I have forgotten my speech and can't think of anything to say.
Leunig

Mister Curly's bedside table
Has a leaning tower of Babel
With a duck to keep it stable
Sitting on the stack

Half-read books with dog-eared pages
Wisdom offered by the sages
Yet the work that most engages
Only gives a quack.

SOCIAL MEDIA WITHOUT ELECTRICITY
I'M FEELING TIRED AND I'VE GOT A HEADACHE
I'M WALKING DOWN THE STREET BREATHING
JUST SAW MY AUNTIE IN THE SHOP
GOING FOR LUNCH NOW
I CANT THINK OF ANYTHING TO SAY
Leunig

WISDOM

How many mouse clicks to wisdom?
What could it possibly be?
Might it be three hundred million?
Could it be something like three?
Or maybe the nature of clicking
Prevents any wisdom at all;
A mouse is for choosing and picking
But wisdom's a hole in the wall.

Leunig

A TREASURY OF ROTTEN LOOKS

THE FROWN

THE SCOWL

STARING DAGGERS

THE GRIMACE

THE GLARE

THE BLACK LOOK

Leunig

DUCKWHISTLE POLITICS.

In every human being
Is something we're not seeing
Down there in the muck
It is the inner duck!

So blow the duckwhistle gently
At least you can blow it mentally
And what you thought was lacking
Will gladly rise up quacking

And with this joyful meekness
And rounded yellow beakness
So beautifully unfurled,
Go out and love the world!

Leunig

SOLILOQUY FOR STRANGE TIMES

The leaders may not know what they're doing — but I do.

We'll keep each other company: this cup, this pot, this tea — and these parts of me.

I'm making tea. Tea For two!

Many things don't work or make sense these days — but the teapot does

One cup for the happy me and one cup for the sadder worried self.

It takes in. It holds. It makes. It pours forth.

Leunig

WHAT GLOOM IS THAT? A GUIDE TO THE GLOOMS.

COMMON HOUSE GLOOM
...a popular and reliable gloom imported from England.

"THE BAD BLANKET"
...a creeping nocturnal gloom causing insomnia and paralysis

"THE BROWN BANANA"
...a cocooning gloom causing a curved downcast stoop.

"THE SLUG"
...a slow, heavy, dragging sort of gloom.

"THE DOUBLE MATTRESS"
...an unwieldy, exhausting gloom for two.

"THE GREY CONSTELLATION"
...a group of frightening glooms in orbit around a person in a spin.

Leunig

Feed the inner duck
Not with human news
Or greedy things that suck,
But give it quiet views;
Comments from the moon,
Opinions from the sky,
The insights of a tune,
The wisdom of a sigh.

The days are getting shorter,
The nights are getting longer,
A part of me is weaker,
Another part is stronger.
Another summer's over,
And we are going under,
We are going home now
To ponder and to wonder.

Leunig